LOGIC
GEOMETRY
PROBLEMS

Wade H. Sherard III

DALE SEYMOUR PUBLICATIONS

*Special recognition and thanks are due to Michele C. Good for all
of her help and expertise in preparing this manuscript for publication.*

Managing Editor: Michael Kane
Project Editor: Joan Gideon
Production Manager: Janet Yearian
Production Coordinator: Leanne Collins
Cover design/text illustrations: Rachel Gage

This book is published by Dale Seymour Publications, an imprint of the Alternative
Publishing Group of Addison-Wesley.

ISBN 0-86651-664-6
Order number DS21211

6 7 8 9 10–MA–03 02 01 00

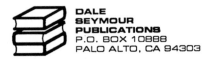

DALE
SEYMOUR
PUBLICATIONS
P.O. BOX 10888
PALO ALTO, CA 94303

This book is printed
on recycled paper.

INTRODUCTION

Logic Geometry Problems is a collection of 50 geometric shape puzzles designed to provide experiences in using problem solving and thinking skills for secondary school students who have a background in geometry. Each puzzle consists of a sequence of ten clues about an unknown convex polygon. The clues, when revealed one at a time, lead students through deductive reasoning to the discovery of the unknown polygon. To solve the puzzles, students must know the definitions and properties of various convex polygons, from triangles to dodecagons, as well as certain skills included in most Algebra I courses. Although students must have the necessary background in geometry to solve the puzzles, the primary emphasis in these activities is on specific problem-solving strategies and thinking skills.

Learning to solve problems is one of the most important reasons that students at all levels should study mathematics. The critical-thinking skills that develop through problem-solving activities in mathematics are useful in solving problems in many different disciplines. The National Council of Teachers of Mathematics (NCTM) recommended in 1980 that problem solving be the focus of school mathematics.[1] NCTM has re-emphasized that recommendation in its *Curriculum and Evaluation Standards for School Mathematics* (1989) by including among its goals for all K-12 students that

1. they become mathematical problem solvers,
2. they learn to reason mathematically, and
3. they learn to communicate mathematically.[2]

The National Council of Supervisors of Mathematics, in its position statement "Essential Mathematics for the Twenty-first Century" (1989), has also included problem solving, communicating mathematical ideas, and mathematical reasoning as three of its twelve components of essential mathematics.[3]

In recent years greater emphasis has been placed on teaching problem solving in the mathematics curriculum. Research shows, however, that students'

---

[1] NCTM, *An Agenda for Action: Recommendations for School Mathematics of the 1980s* (Reston, VA: NCTM, 1980), p. 1. See also *Problem Solving in School Mathematics*, 1980 Yearbook (Reston, VA: NCTM, 1980).

[2] NCTM, *Curriculum and Evaluation Standards for School Mathematics* (Reston, VA: NCTM, 1989), pp. 5–6.

[3] NCSM, "Essential Mathematics for the Twenty-first Century," *Mathematics Teacher* 82 (September 1989), pp. 470–74.

problem-solving skills are still considerably weaker than their computational skills. Much more needs to be done to improve students' abilities to solve problems and to think critically. Students especially need to be exposed to problem-solving activities in many different contexts.

The work of George Pólya has been a dominant influence on the teaching of problem solving in mathematics. Pólya recommends a four-phase procedure to provide structure and guidance in solving a problem:

Phase I: Understanding the problem
Phase II: Devising a plan
Phase III: Carrying out the plan
Phase IV: Looking back

These four phases, and suggestions for implementing them, are discussed in detail in two of Pólya's books *How to Solve It* (first published in 1945) and *Mathematical Discovery.* [4] The impact of these books on the teaching of problem solving has been enormous. Analyses of articles, books, and current mathematics curricula concerning problem solving reveal many of Pólya's ideas, especially these four phases for solving a problem.

The second phase, devising a plan, is the one that is probably most difficult for students. The following strategies for this phase (most of which are directly attributable to Pólya) are especially appropriate for solving the geometry puzzles in this collection:

1. Make a list of possibilities. Can the list be modified or reduced, given the conditions of the problem?

2. Carefully consider the conditions of the problem. What new information can be derived from the conditions? Are all the conditions necessary? Have all the essential conditions of the problem been taken into account?

3. Draw pictures that satisfy the conditions and data of the problem.

4. Think of a related problem or concept. Are there definitions, properties, or theorems that are related to the unknowns, the data, and the conditions of the problem?

5. Consider a similar problem. Could its method of solution be used?

6. Write an equation involving the unknown(s) and the conditions of the problem. Can the equation be solved for the unknown(s)?

The puzzles written for this collection provide students with ample opportunities to develop and use these particular problem-solving skills. In fact, most of the puzzles require that several of these strategies be used.

---

[4] Pólya, George, *How to Solve It*, 2nd ed. (Princeton, NJ: Princeton University Press, 1973), p. 172; *Mathematical Discovery*, combined ed. (New York: John Wiley & Sons, 1981).

Although the fourth phase, looking back, is probably the most neglected phase in the teaching of problem solving, it needs to be emphasized. The following key questions for this phase of Pólya's procedure are directly applicable to the puzzles in this collection:

1. Is the solution reasonable? Does it make sense? Does the solution meet all the conditions of the problem? Can the solution be checked?
2. Is there another method for solving the problem? How does it compare to the first method?
3. Is the method of solution useful for other problems? Should the method of solution be remembered for future use?

The puzzles in this collection provide students with many opportunities for asking these questions.

Pólya insists that the teaching of problem solving must include abundant experience in solving specific problems as well as careful study of the solution process itself. Students who solve or attempt to solve puzzles in this collection will gain valuable experience in solving problems, and with the appropriate guidance from their teacher, will begin to study the general process of problem solving.

In order to solve these puzzles, students need to have a good background in the geometry of convex polygons. While some of the basic definitions of these polygons and their properties are part of the standard mathematics curriculum for grades 6–8, all the definitions and properties are part of the standard high school geometry curriculum. For some of the puzzles, students need to be able to use elementary algebraic techniques that are included in standard Algebra I courses.

DEFINITIONS

These puzzles involve only *convex* polygons. The following terms related to convex polygons are used in the puzzles; students will need to be familiar with them.

Triangles	right triangle; isosceles triangle; equilateral triangle; isosceles right triangle; 30°–60° right triangle
Quadrilaterals	parallelogram; rectangle; square, rhombus; trapezoid; right trapezoid; isosceles trapezoid; kite
N-gons for $n \geq 5$	pentagon; hexagon; heptagon; octagon; nonagon; decagon; dodecagon; equilateral polygon; equiangular polygon; regular polygon
Angles	acute angle; obtuse angle; right angle; exterior angle; supplementary angles; complementary angles

Other terms that students will need to know include the following:

diagonal   line of symmetry
angle bisector   rotational symmetry
perpendicular bisector   inscribed polygon
altitude   diameter of a circle
perimeter   chord of a circle
area

Not all definitions in geometry are standard. The following definitions apply in these puzzles:

An *isosceles triangle* is a triangle having exactly two congruent sides.

A *trapezoid* is a quadrilateral having exactly one pair of parallel sides.

A *kite* is a convex quadrilateral having two pairs of congruent consecutive sides with no side common to both pairs.

An *exterior angle* of a polygon is an angle that forms a linear pair with an angle of the polygon. Note that a polygon has *two* congruent exterior angles at each vertex.

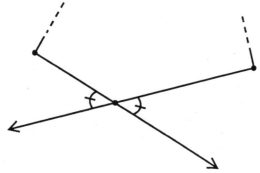

FORMULAS

Students will need to know area formulas for rectangles, squares, triangles, and trapezoids to solve some of the puzzles.

PROPERTIES AND THEOREMS

The puzzle clues draw on many properties and theorems related to convex polygons. These are stated below, classified according to whether they apply to triangles, quadrilaterals, *n*-gons, or circles.

Triangles
1. The sum of the measures of the angles of a triangle is 180°.
2. The acute angles of a right triangle are complementary.
3. The sum of the lengths of any two sides of a triangle is greater than the length of the third side.

4. The angle bisectors of a triangle are concurrent.
5. In a right triangle, the square of the length of the hypotenuse equals the sum of the squares of the lengths of the other two sides (Pythagorean Theorem), and conversely.
6. In a 30°–60° right triangle, the length of the hypotenuse is twice the length of the shorter leg, and the longer leg is $\sqrt{3}$ times the length of the shorter leg.

Quadrilaterals
1. The sum of the measures of the angles of a quadrilateral is 360°.
2. A quadrilateral having both pairs of opposite sides congruent is a parallelogram; and conversely.
3. A quadrilateral having both pairs of opposite angles congruent is a parallelogram; and conversely.
4. A quadrilateral having its consecutive angles supplementary is a parallelogram; and conversely.
5. A quadrilateral having a pair of opposite sides that are parallel and congruent is a parallelogram.
6. A quadrilateral having diagonals that bisect each other is a parallelogram; and conversely.
7. A parallelogram with a right angle is a rectangle.
8. The diagonals of a rectangle bisect each other and are congruent.
9. The diagonals of a rhombus bisect each other, are perpendicular, and bisect the angles that they join.
10. The diagonals of a square bisect each other, are perpendicular, bisect the angles that they join, and are congruent.
11. The diagonals of an isosceles trapezoid are congruent.
12. The diagonals of a kite are perpendicular.
13. The principal diagonal of a kite (i.e., the diagonal that lies on the line of symmetry) bisects the other diagonal and bisects the angles that it joins.

Convex n-gons
1. A convex n-gon has $\dfrac{n(n-1)}{2}$ pairs of angles.
2. A convex n-gon has $\dfrac{n(n-3)}{2}$ diagonals.
3. The sum of the measures of the angles of a convex n-gon is $(n-2) \times 180°$.
4. Each angle of a regular convex n-gon measures $\dfrac{(n-2) \times 180°}{n}$.
5. The sum of the measures of the exterior angles of a convex polygon, one at each vertex, is 360°.

Circles
1. Congruent chords of a circle determine congruent central angles; and conversely.
2. An angle inscribed in a semicircle is a right angle.
3. If a quadrilateral is inscribed in a circle, its opposite angles are supplementary.

ALGEBRAIC SKILLS

To solve these logic geometry puzzles, students will in some cases need to be able to do the following:

1. Evaluate algebraic expressions.
2. Solve linear equations with one variable.
3. Solve simple quadratic equations with one variable.
4. Find positive integer solutions to a linear equation with two variables.
5. Identify and use an arithmetic sequence.

DOING LOGIC GEOMETRY PUZZLES

Each puzzle in this collection consists of a list of ten clues. The clues are to be considered one at a time, in sequence. Each new clue provides more information about the unknown polygon. Students may want to use another sheet of paper to reveal each new clue and to cover the remaining clues as they work. The basic objective of the puzzle is to discover the unknown polygon by using the least possible number of clues from the list. The clues, which give information about the unknown polygon, allow students to determine through deductive reasoning precisely what kind of polygon is being described. Once students feel they have correctly identified the exact polygon, they can check the remaining clues against that shape to confirm the solution to the puzzle.

In determining the solution to a puzzle, the polygon named must be the most specific kind of polygon that uniquely satisfies the clues in the list at that point. For example, if the solution to a puzzle is a parallelogram, then the clues must rule out the possibility that the polygon could also be a rectangle or a rhombus or a square. The puzzles describe the following types of convex polygons:

equilateral triangle	regular pentagon
isosceles triangle	equilateral hexagon
isosceles right triangle	equiangular hexagon
30°–60° right triangle	regular hexagon
parallelogram	equilateral heptagon
rectangle	regular heptagon
rhombus	equilateral octagon
square	equiangular octagon
trapezoid	regular octagon

In looking back at the solution, the clues that remain after the unknown polygon has been determined serve as a partial check of the solution. Can this method of solution be used to solve similar puzzles? Yes; so it should be remembered as a possible strategy for use when a similar puzzle is encountered.

Sample Puzzle D

1. It is a closed figure with straight sides.

2. Each of its sides has the same length.

3. It has two right angles.

4. Its other angles measure either 120° or 150°.

5. Each right angle is consecutive with only 150° angles.

6. It has more 150° angles than it has 120° angles.

7. It has only one 120° angle.

8. It has only one line of symmetry.

9. The sum of the measures of all of its angles is 900°.

10. It has two pairs of parallel sides.

Suggested Solution to Sample Puzzle D by Clues

Clue 1   The shape is a polygon.

Clue 2   The polygon is equilateral.

Clues 3, 4   Let a be the number of 150° angles and b be the number of 120° angles. Use the fact that the sum of the measures of the angles of a convex n-gon is $(n - 2) \times 180°$ to write the equation

$$90(2) + 150a + 120b = (a + b + 2 - 2)180$$

$$180 + 150a + 120b = 180a + 180b$$

$$30a + 60b = 180$$

$$a + 2b = 6$$

Since a and b must be positive integers, there are only two possible solutions to the equation:

a	b
2	2
4	1

So, the unknown polygon could be either an equilateral hexagon or an equilateral heptagon.

Clue 5   This clue eliminates the solution $a = 2$, $b = 2$. Because the polygon has two right angles, at least three 150° angles are needed to satisfy this condition:

150°   90°   150°   90°   150° ... , and $a \geq 3$

Thus, the only possible solution to the equation is $a = 4$, $b = 1$, so the unknown polygon *appears* to be an equilateral heptagon.

Does such a heptagon exist? And if it does, what is the sequence of its angles? Starting with the 120° angle, the only two possible sequences of its angles are these:

120°   150°   90°   150°   90°   150°   150°
120°   150°   90°   150°   150°   90°   150°

The first sequence does not form a heptagon, because the subsequence of angles 150°, 90°, 150°, 90°, 150°, with equal side lengths, closes up to form a hexagon with alternating 90° and 150° angles.

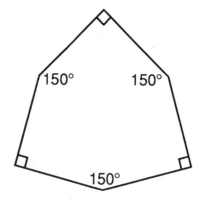

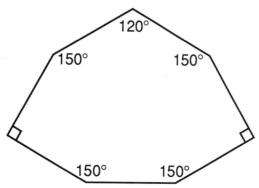

The second sequence yields an equilateral heptagon.

Clues 6–10   These conditions confirm that the unknown polygon is an equilateral heptagon.

The key strategy for solving this puzzle is writing an equation for the sum of the measures of the angles of the unknown polygon in terms of its unknown numbers of 120° angles and 150° angles, and then finding possible solutions of that equation. Other strategies used include deriving more information about the unknown polygon from other conditions in the clues, and considering definitions, properties, or theorems related to concepts in the clues. Drawing pictures that satisfy clues 1–5 helps in determining the solution.

Puzzle 1

"We really thought he'd had a brilliant breakthrough, but now we're not so sure!"

1. It is a closed figure with four straight sides.

2. It has both long sides and short sides.

3. Its two short sides have the same length.

4. Its two long sides have the same length.

5. Some of its angles are not congruent.

6. Two of its angles measure 140°.

7. Its other two angles measure 40°.

8. Its two short sides are parallel.

9. Its two long sides are parallel.

10. Its diagonals bisect each other.

Puzzle 2

1. It is a closed figure with straight sides.

2. It has two acute angles.

3. It has no diagonals.

4. One of its angles is not acute.

5. It has two sides of length *s*.

6. It has a pair of complementary angles.

7. It has a right angle.

8. Its acute angles are congruent.

9. Each acute angle measures 45°.

10. Its area is one-half the area of a square with sides of length *s*.

"Don't tell me you used no glue at all?"

Puzzle 3

"Happy Birthday, dear Pythagoras, Happy Birthday to you!"

1. It is a closed figure with four straight sides.

2. Two of its sides are parallel.

3. Its other two sides are parallel.

4. It has two angles that are congruent.

5. It has two more angles that are congruent.

6. Its diagonals bisect each other.

7. It has a right angle.

8. Its diagonals are not perpendicular.

9. Its diagonals have the same length.

10. All of its angles are right angles.

Puzzle 4

1.   It is a closed figure with four straight sides.

2.   One of its angles measures 45°.

3.   One of its angles measures 135°.

4.   Another angle measures 45°.

5.   Another angle measures 135°.

6.   Two of its sides are parallel.

7.   Its other two sides are parallel.

8.   All of its sides have the same length.

9.   Its diagonals bisect each other.

10. Its diagonals are perpendicular.

The first pyramid scheme.

LOGIC GEOMETRY PROBLEMS © DALE SEYMOUR PUBLICATIONS

Puzzle 5

"Originally I just planned to make it one basic rectangular prism topped by a truncated pyramid, but something happened when I faxed the plans..."

1. It is a closed figure with four straight sides.

2. Two of its angles are congruent.

3. Two of its sides are parallel.

4. Two of its sides have the same length.

5. Its parallel sides have the same length.

6. Its opposite sides are congruent.

7. It has a right angle.

8. Its consecutive sides have the same length.

9. All of its angles are right angles.

10. All of its sides have the same length.

Puzzle 6

"Why do we call it a teepee when it's really a hexagonal pyramid?"

1. It is a closed figure with straight sides.

2. It has no right angles.

3. It has no parallel sides.

4. It has no diagonals.

5. It has an exterior angle that measures 120°.

6. It has three lines of symmetry.

7. Each of its angle bisectors contains an altitude.

8. Each of its exterior angles measures 120°.

9. All of its sides have the same length.

10. All of its angles are congruent.

Puzzle 7

1. It is a closed figure with straight sides.

2. It has a pair of opposite sides that are congruent and parallel.

3. It has another pair of opposite sides that are congruent and parallel.

4. Its consecutive sides are not congruent.

5. The sum of the measures of all of its angles is 360°.

6. It has no right angles.

7. Its consecutive angles are supplementary.

8. Its opposite angles are congruent.

9. Its diagonals bisect each other.

10. Its diagonals are not congruent.

Puzzle 8

"What do you mean you have a piece left over!"

1. It is a closed figure with straight sides.

2. The sum of the measures of all of its angles is less than 360°.

3. One of its angle bisectors lies on the perpendicular bisector of one of its sides.

4. It has a pair of complementary angles.

5. One of its exterior angles is congruent to one of its angles.

6. None of its exterior angles are acute.

7. It has six exterior angles.

8. One of its angle bisectors lies on its only line of symmetry.

9. Two of its sides are perpendicular.

10. Two of its sides are congruent.

Puzzle 9

1. It is a closed figure with straight sides.

2. It has only two diagonals.

3. Its diagonals bisect each other.

4. Its opposite angles are bisected by its diagonals.

5. Both of its diagonals lie on lines of symmetry.

6. Its diagonals have the same length.

7. Its diagonals are perpendicular.

8. It has two pairs of parallel sides.

9. All of its sides have the same length.

10. All of its angles are right angles.

"But the drawing didn't say top view or bottom view."

Puzzle 10

1. It is a closed figure with straight sides.

2. It has sides of two different lengths.

3. Each of its short sides has length $2r$.

4. Each of its long sides has length $3r$.

5. Its perimeter is $10r$.

6. Its short sides are perpendicular to its long sides.

7. Its opposite angles are congruent.

8. Its long sides are parallel.

9. Its short sides are parallel.

10. Its area is $6r^2$.

"Someday they'll pay big money for an arm like that!"

LOGIC GEOMETRY PROBLEMS © DALE SEYMOUR PUBLICATIONS

Puzzle 11

1. It is a closed figure with straight sides.

2. One of its angle bisectors lies on the perpendicular bisector of one of its sides.

3. Another of its angle bisectors lies on the perpendicular bisector of one of its sides.

4. Its angle bisectors are concurrent.

5. The sum of the measures of all of its angles is 180°.

6. It has no obtuse angles.

7. It has 120° rotational symmetry.

8. It has 240° rotational symmetry.

9. Its exterior angles are congruent.

10. All of its sides are congruent.

NEW CHURCHSKI
WORKING MODEL

"I still think the broccoli is better than the onions."

Puzzle 12

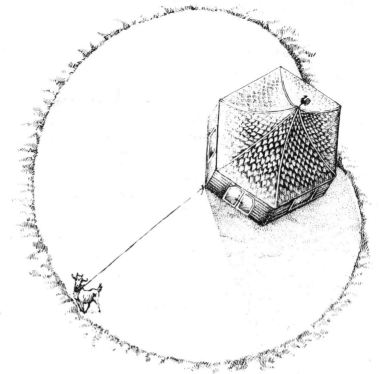

Oh, for a bungee cord.

1. It is a closed figure with straight sides.

2. Each of its long sides has length 8m.

3. Each of its short sides has length 4m.

4. It has only two diagonals.

5. Its perimeter is 24m.

6. Its diagonals bisect each other.

7. It has a diagonal of length 9m.

8. Its long sides are parallel.

9. Its short sides are parallel.

10. It has no right angles.

LOGIC GEOMETRY PROBLEMS © DALE SEYMOUR PUBLICATIONS

Puzzle 13

1. It is a closed figure with straight sides.

2. Each of its angle bisectors lies on a line of symmetry.

3. Each of its angle bisectors contains a diagonal.

4. It has eight exterior angles.

5. It has a pair of complementary angles.

6. It has four pairs of supplementary angles.

7. It has no right angles.

8. It has two 45° angles.

9. It has two 135° angles.

10. All of its sides are congruent.

"Señor Escalator, this should be a moving experience!"

Puzzle 14

"Well, nobody's perfect."

1. It is a closed figure with straight sides.

2. It has no parallel sides.

3. It has no diagonals.

4. It has no obtuse angles.

5. It has a pair of complementary angles.

6. The length of its longest side is twice the length of its shortest side.

7. None of its sides have the same length.

8. None of its angles have the same measure.

9. It has a right angle.

10. It has a 30° angle.

Puzzle 15

1. It is a closed figure with straight sides.

2. It has six pairs of angles.

3. Its diagonals have length 13w.

4. Its consecutive angles are supplementary.

5. Its area is 60w^2.

6. Its opposite angles are supplementary.

7. Its opposite sides are parallel.

8. It has two sides of length 5w.

9. It has two sides of length 12w.

10. It has four right angles.

"I know it's a great problem, but I would just tear down one of the bridges."

Puzzle 16

"Great! But do you think the Queen will like it?"

1. It is a closed figure with straight sides.

2. All of its exterior angles are congruent.

3. It has eight exterior angles.

4. Each of its angle bisectors lies on a line of symmetry.

5. Each of its diagonals lies on a line of symmetry.

6. Any two of its angles are supplementary.

7. Each diagonal partitions it into two congruent isosceles triangles.

8. It has a pair of parallel sides.

9. Its other two sides are parallel.

10. All of its angles are right angles.

LOGIC GEOMETRY PROBLEMS © DALE SEYMOUR PUBLICATIONS

Puzzle 21

1. It is a closed figure with straight sides.

2. It can be inscribed in a circle.

3. Each of its diagonals is also a diameter of the circle in which it can be inscribed.

4. Its diagonals are not perpendicular to each other.

5. It has a pair of opposite sides that are congruent.

6. It has another pair of opposite sides that are congruent.

7. It has two pairs of opposite angles that are supplementary.

8. It has four pairs of consecutive angles that are supplementary.

9. Its consecutive sides are not congruent.

10. It has four right angles.

"Hey, bub. You got a one track mind!"

Puzzle 22

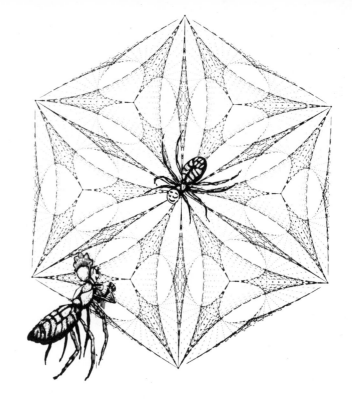

"Oh son, I always knew you were different!"

1. It is a closed figure with four straight sides.

2. It has two long sides and two short sides.

3. Its two long sides are parallel.

4. Two of its angles are right angles.

5. Its two long sides do not have the same length.

6. Its two long sides make right angles with one of the short sides.

7. Its two short sides are not parallel.

8. Its two short sides do not have the same length.

9. Its diagonals do not have the same length.

10. It has only two right angles.

Puzzle 23

1. It is a closed figure with straight sides.

2. It has a side of length s.

3. It has a side of length $2s$.

4. Some of its angles are acute.

5. The sum of the measures of all of its angles is less than 360°.

6. It has a side of length $\sqrt{3}\,s$.

7. Its area is $\dfrac{\sqrt{3}\,s^2}{2}$.

8. It has a 30° angle opposite the side of length s.

9. It has a 60° angle opposite the side of length $\sqrt{3}\,s$.

10. Its two shorter sides are perpendicular.

"Do you really think it matters <u>which</u> side of the rectangle we put the columns on?"

Puzzle 24

"I told you to stack them in the shape of a dodecahedron!"

1. It is a closed figure with straight sides.

2. It has only two diagonals.

3. Its diagonals bisect each other.

4. Its diagonals have the same length.

5. Its diagonals are not perpendicular.

6. Neither of its diagonals lies on a line of symmetry.

7. Its opposite angles are not bisected by its diagonals.

8. It has two congruent long sides.

9. It has two congruent short sides.

10. It has four right angles.

LOGIC GEOMETRY PROBLEMS © DALE SEYMOUR PUBLICATIONS

Puzzle 25

1. It is a closed figure with four straight sides.

2. Two of its sides are parallel.

3. Its other two sides are parallel.

4. It has consecutive angles that are supplementary.

5. It has consecutive angles that are congruent.

6. It has consecutive sides that have the same length.

7. It has a right angle.

8. All of its sides have the same length.

9. Its diagonals are perpendicular.

10. Its diagonals have the same length.

"Hey! That's a <u>cool</u> hemisphere"

Puzzle 26

"Don't tell me you used no glue at all?"

1. It is a closed figure with four straight sides.

2. It has two long sides and two short sides.

3. Its two short sides have the same length.

4. Its two long sides have the same length.

5. Its short sides are perpendicular to its long sides.

6. Its opposite angles are supplementary.

7. It has no parallel sides.

8. Its diagonals are perpendicular.

9. Its diagonals do not bisect each other.

10. One of its diagonals lies on its line of symmetry.

Puzzle 27

1. It is a closed figure with straight sides.

2. Its angle bisectors lie on its lines of symmetry.

3. None of its diagonals lie on its lines of symmetry.

4. It has no right angles.

5. It has no parallel sides.

6. Each of its sides has the same length.

7. Each of its angles measures 108°.

8. It has five lines of symmetry.

9. It has five diagonals.

10. Its diagonals form a five-pointed star.

"But the drawing didn't say top view or bottom view."

Puzzle 28

"Happy Birthday, dear Pythagoras, Happy Birthday to you!"

1. It is a closed figure with straight sides.

2. It can be partitioned into eight equilateral triangles, each having side length c.

3. It has no right angles.

4. It has two 60° angles.

5. It has two 120° angles.

6. Its perimeter is $8c$.

7. One of its sides has length $3c$.

8. It has two sides of length $2c$.

9. It has one pair of sides that are parallel.

10. It has only two pairs of supplementary consecutive angles.

Puzzle 29

1. It is a closed figure with straight sides.

2. It has only two diagonals.

3. Its diagonals are perpendicular.

4. Its diagonals are not congruent.

5. It has a diagonal that lies on a line of symmetry.

6. It has a diagonal that bisects the angles it joins.

7. It has a diagonal that bisects the other diagonal.

8. It has a diagonal that does not bisect the other diagonal.

9. It has no parallel sides.

10. It has two pairs of consecutive congruent sides.

Puzzle 30

"We really thought he'd had a brilliant breakthrough, but now we're not so sure!"

1. It is a closed figure with straight sides.

2. It has opposite sides that are parallel.

3. Its opposite sides have the same length.

4. All of its angles are congruent.

5. It has no supplementary angles.

6. All of its sides have the same length.

7. The sum of the measures of all of its angles is 1080°.

8. It has 28 pairs of angles.

9. Each of its angles measures 135°.

10. It has eight sides.

LOGIC GEOMETRY PROBLEMS © DALE SEYMOUR PUBLICATIONS

Puzzle 31

1. It is a closed figure with straight sides.

2. It has sides of two different lengths.

3. Its long sides have length 7*t*.

4. Its short sides have length 2*t*.

5. Its perimeter is 30*t*.

6. Its long sides are parallel to each other.

7. All of its angles are congruent.

8. Each of its angles measures 144°.

9. It has four pairs of parallel short sides.

10. It has only two lines of symmetry.

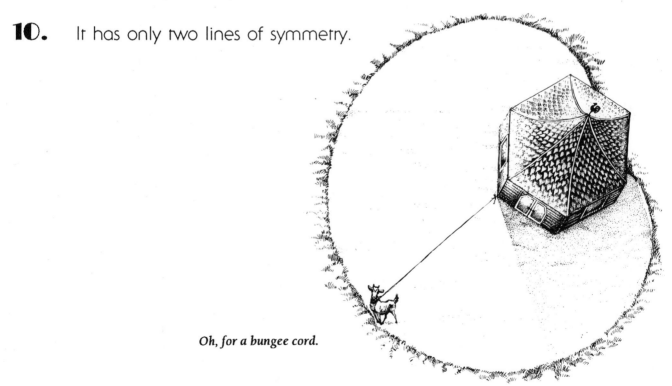

Oh, for a bungee cord.

Puzzle 32

"Well, nobody's perfect."

1. It is a closed figure with straight sides.

2. Its smallest angle measures 45°.

3. The measures of its four consecutive angles form an arithmetic sequence.

4. None of its angles are right angles.

5. It has an angle measuring 105°.

6. It has two acute angles.

7. The common difference in the arithmetic sequence of its consecutive angles is 30°.

8. None of its sides are congruent.

9. It has two pairs of supplementary angles.

10. It has one pair of parallel sides.

Puzzle 33

1. It is a closed figure with straight sides.

2. It has sides of two different lengths.

3. One of its angles measures 135°.

4. Another of its angles measures 135°.

5. Its 135° angles are not consecutive angles.

6. Its other angles are right angles.

7. It has two sides that are parallel.

8. It has ten pairs of angles.

9. The sum of the measures of all of its angles is 540°.

10. It can be partitioned into two congruent right trapezoids.

"Originally I just planned to make it one basic
rectangular prism topped by a truncated pyramid,
but something happened when I faxed the plans..."

Puzzle 34

"Señor Escalator, this should be a moving experience!"

1. It is a closed figure with straight sides.

2. It can be inscribed in a circle.

3. The sum of the measures of all of its angles is 1800°.

4. Its sides are congruent chords of the circle in which it can be inscribed.

5. It has 30° rotational symmetry.

6. Connecting every fourth vertex with line segments forms an equilateral triangle.

7. Connecting every second vertex with line segments forms a regular hexagon.

8. Each of its angles measures 150°.

9. It has six pairs of parallel sides.

10. It can be partitioned into 12 congruent isosceles triangles.

Puzzle 39

1. It is a closed figure with straight sides.

2. It has opposite sides that are congruent.

3. It has opposite sides that are parallel.

4. It has an angle measuring 120°.

5. All of its sides are congruent.

6. All of its angles are congruent.

7. The sum of the measures of all of its angles is 720°.

8. It can be inscribed in a circle.

9. It can be partitioned into six equilateral triangles.

10. It has six sides.

"Okay Möbius, what are we going to do with these?"

Puzzle 40

"I know it's a great problem, but I would just tear down one of the bridges."

1.   It is a closed figure with straight sides.

2.   Some of its angles measure 120°.

3.   Its other angles measure 150°.

4.   Each of its sides has the same length.

5.   Its angles alternate.

6.   It has four lines of symmetry.

7.   It has 20 diagonals.

8.   It has 90° rotational symmetry.

9.   It has four pairs of parallel sides.

10.   The sum of the measures of all of its angles is 1080°.

   LOGIC GEOMETRY PROBLEMS © DALE SEYMOUR PUBLICATIONS

Puzzle 41

1. It is a closed figure with straight sides.

2. It has no parallel sides.

3. It has no perpendicular sides.

4. All of its sides are congruent.

5. Each of its angle bisectors is perpendicular to one of its sides.

6. All of its angles are congruent.

7. It has 14 diagonals.

8. The sum of the measures of all of its angles is 900°.

9. It has seven lines of symmetry.

10. It has seven sides.

"Who says they always have to be vertical?"

Puzzle 42

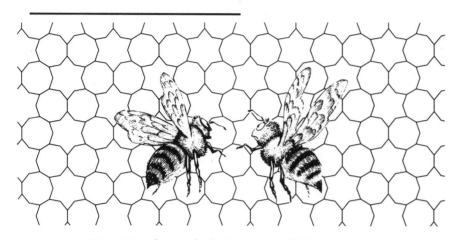

"Great! But do you think the Queen will like it?"

1. It is a closed figure with straight sides.

2. It can be inscribed in a circle.

3. It has a diagonal that is also a diameter of the circle in which it can be inscribed.

4. Its two diagonals are perpendicular.

5. It has a diagonal that is not a diameter of the circle in which it can be inscribed.

6. It has a pair of consecutive sides that are perpendicular.

7. It has another pair of consecutive sides that are perpendicular.

8. It has two pairs of supplementary angles.

9. It has a pair of consecutive sides that are congruent.

10. It has another pair of consecutive sides that are congruent.

  LOGIC GEOMETRY PROBLEMS © DALE SEYMOUR PUBLICATIONS

Puzzle 43

1. It is a closed figure with straight sides.

2. It can be inscribed in a circle.

3. Its sides are congruent chords of the circle in which it can be inscribed.

4. It has only four diagonals that are also diameters of the circle in which it can be inscribed.

5. It has 45° rotational symmetry.

6. It has 16 diagonals that are not diameters of the circle in which it can be inscribed.

7. Some of its diagonals are parallel.

8. Some of its diagonals are perpendicular.

9. It has four pairs of parallel sides.

10. It can be partitioned into eight congruent isosceles triangles.

The first pyramid scheme.

Puzzle 44

"Someday they'll pay big money for an arm like that!"

1. It is a closed figure with straight sides.

2. It has three right angles.

3. All of its perpendicular sides have the same length.

4. It has no parallel sides.

5. All of its other angles are congruent.

6. Its right angles alternate with its other angles.

7. It has exactly nine diagonals.

8. Three of its diagonals form an equilateral triangle.

9. Another three of its diagonals form a different equilateral triangle.

10. Its six sides have the same length.

Puzzle 45

1. It is a closed figure with straight sides.

2. All of its sides have the same length.

3. None of its sides are perpendicular.

4. Some of its angles measure 120°.

5. Its other angles measure 150°.

6. Any three of its consecutive angles include one 120° angle.

7. It has twice as many angles of one size as it does of the other size.

8. The sum of the measures of all of its angles is 1260°.

9. It has six 150° angles.

10. It has nine sides.

NEW CHURCHSKI
WORKING MODEL

"The onions look pretty nice, but did you try the zucchini?"

Puzzle 46

"What do you mean you have a piece left over!"

1. It is a closed figure with straight sides.

2. It has consecutive sides of lengths $7x$ and $24x$.

3. It has consecutive sides of lengths $18x$ and $24x$.

4. The sum of the measures of all of its angles is 360°.

5. Its diagonal joining the consecutive sides of lengths $18x$ and $24x$ has length $30x$.

6. Its other diagonal has length $25x$.

7. Its area is $300x^2$.

8. It has two parallel sides.

9. It has two right angles.

10. Its fourth side has length $\sqrt{697}\,x$.

Puzzle 47

1. It is a closed figure with straight sides.

2. All of its sides are congruent.

3. The diagonals that join its alternate vertices are congruent.

4. It has 35 diagonals.

5. It has diagonals of four different lengths.

6. The sum of the measures of all of its angles is 1440°.

7. It has five pairs of parallel sides.

8. It has 20 congruent exterior angles.

9. It has 36° rotational symmetry.

10. Each of its angles measures 144°.

"That's your perspective!"

Puzzle 48

"I told you to stack them in the shape of a dodecahedron!"

1. It is a closed figure with straight sides.

2. It has sides of two different lengths.

3. It has short sides, each having length 24*d*.

4. It has long sides, each having length 30*d*.

5. Its perimeter is 216*d*.

6. Its long sides and its short sides alternate.

7. Each of its exterior angles measures 45°.

8. It has two pairs of parallel long sides.

9. It has two pairs of parallel short sides.

10. Each of its angles measures 135°.

Puzzle 49

1.   It is a closed figure with straight sides.

2.   One of its angles measures 150°.

3.   Another of its angles measures 150°.

4.   It has two right angles.

5.   All of its sides have the same length.

6.   It has one line of symmetry.

7.   It has an angle measuring 60°.

8.   One of its sides is perpendicular to two of its other sides.

9.   It can be partitioned into a square and an equilateral triangle.

10. It has five sides.

"Why don't you go do your symmetry homework and then come back and try again?"

Puzzle 50

"Hey! Great nest! But laying eggs like a triangular prism is not going to be easy!"

1. It is a closed figure with straight sides.

2. Each of its sides has the same length.

3. It has two right angles.

4. Each of its other angles measures 135°.

5. One of its diagonals lies on a line of symmetry.

6. It has a line of symmetry that does not contain a diagonal.

7. It has 15 pairs of angles.

8. It can be partitioned into a rectangle and two congruent isosceles triangles.

9. It can be partitioned into two congruent isosceles trapezoids.

10. It has three pairs of parallel sides.

   LOGIC GEOMETRY PROBLEMS © DALE SEYMOUR PUBLICATIONS